ON A
TRAIN JOURNEY

Station

This I-SPY book belongs to: ANITA AND FAMILY!

Introduction

Almost everyone loves to take a train journey. As well as the excitement of reaching your destination – perhaps you are going on holiday to the seaside – railway stations and the trains themselves are full of fascinating things to see from the moment you get to the station, before you start your trip, to arriving at the other end. At a big station, there is all the hustle and bustle of travel, as well as a range of shops to browse around, and the various kinds of refreshments to be had. You might use a local train just to get to school, or you could use a service to take you from one end of the country to the other. You can use a laptop on some trains, and you can often find buffet carriages or trolleys selling food and drink on board, including full meals on those trains that have a restaurant car.

There are now nearly thirty separate train companies operating regular passenger and freight trains on Britain's national railway system. And there are underground lines and metros, special trains and steam railways, too. So look out for a wonderful variety of trains, locomotives and carriages, all in their different colours, as you travel the country.

And, as you travel (sometimes at speeds of up to 125 miles an hour (200 km/h)), there is so much to see on a train journey provided you keep your eyes open. It's fun to find out about the world as it rushes by, and you'll be surprised by all the fascinating things you'll discover. Of course, if you travel by car, you must not distract the driver but, on a train journey, all the family can join in the I-Spy fun.

How to use your I-SPY book

There are so many things you could look out for on a train journey that it's hard to know where to begin, what to include, or what to leave out. Your I-Spy on a Train Journey book takes you from your arrival at the station, through the station itself, along the journey, and reaching your destination, with some ideas of what you might see along the way.
You need 1000 points to send off for your I-Spy certificate (see page 64) but that is not too difficult because there are masses of points in every book. As you make each I-Spy, write your score in the box and, where there is a question, double your score if you can answer it. Check your answer against the correct one on page 63.

2

Stations, big or small, are always well sign-posted to help travellers get there easily.

You might arrive to find yourself under a canopy which protects travellers from the rain.

 I - SPY points: 10

This sign shows the way to the station and to the city centre.

 I - SPY points: 5

Some stations have elaborate fountains in their forecourt.

 I - SPY points: 10

This sign shows the way to the station car park.

 I - SPY points: 5

MICHELIN

Many railway stations have large car parks. Double points if the station is a Parkway built specially to serve motorists from a wide area.

 I - SPY points: 5

After parking, be sure to pay and display!

 I - SPY points: 5

As well as cars, stations have places to park motorbikes…

 I - SPY points: 5

…and for bicycles.

 I - SPY points: 5

Outside the station, there is usually a large sign showing its name, often with the famous double-arrow symbol.

 I - SPY points: 5

All stations have name boards on the platform so that travellers arriving can see where they are.

I - SPY points: 5

Fast moving trains travel through some stations. It is important to stand well back and observe the safety instructions.

 I - SPY points: 5

You will need to buy a valid ticket for your journey.

 I - SPY points: 5

Station Signs

All stations now have a non-smoking policy...

 I - SPY points: 5

...and most have security cameras.

 I - SPY points: 5

Many stations have wheelchair facilities...

 I - SPY points: 5

...and if you need to ask for help, it can be found at the touch of a button!

 I - SPY points: 10

This very famous platform might not really exist!

 I - SPY points: 20

This is a traditional wayside country station…

 I - SPY points: 10

…often stations have beautiful flower displays.

 I - SPY points: 10

Whilst waiting for a train, you can always use the Waiting Room.

 I - SPY points: 5

This platform is almost empty as the last passenger gets ready to board.

 I - SPY points: 5

You may need to weigh your luggage (or yourself).

 I - SPY points: 10

Most platforms have a digital display telling you the time of the next arrival.

 I - SPY points: 5

You can bring your bicycle onto the platform of some stations and use the Cycle Park

 I - SPY points: 5

...but if you want to take your bicycle with you, you'll need to find the special loading point.

 I - SPY points: 10

This is a special station. It has the longest place name in Europe!
Do you know where it is?

I - SPY points: 30, double with answer

9

There are many different types of bridges spanning the railway tracks. Here are a selection of different types for both pedestrians, and for road traffic to cross from one side of a main line to the other.

This overbridge is right on the road side.

I - SPY points: 15

This bridge is enclosed, keeping you dry when it rains.

I - SPY points: 5

A traditional footbridge linking the platforms.

I - SPY points: 5

Here you can see a road bridge over the rails.

I - SPY points: 5

Large stations always have a travel centre where you can buy tickets and make reservations.

 I - SPY points: 10

You can get all the information you need to plan your journey.

◯ **I - SPY** points: 10

Many stations have an information booth where you can ask for assistance...

◯ **I - SPY** points: 10

...or check on the information display.

 I - SPY points: 5

You will need to check your departure time…

I - SPY points: 5

…and make that vital connection.

I - SPY points: 5

You can use the self-service ticket machines to speed up buying your tickets.

I - SPY points: 5

You may choose to speak to someone and buy your ticket...

I - SPY points: 5

...which may involve standing in a queue.

I - SPY points: 5

Staff are always willing to offer help and assistance.

I - SPY points: 5

When you have bought your ticket, you will need to know which platform to go to.

I - SPY points: 5

Full details of departure times and destination are displayed on large electronic boards.

 I - SPY points: 5

You can check if the train will depart on time...

 I - SPY points: 5

...and what platform it will leave from.

 I - SPY points: 10

There are a variety of ways to tell the time at a train station.

Some have clocks outside.

 I - SPY points: 10

Some have analogue clocks inside on the concourse.

 I - SPY points: 10

There may be a digital clock on the platform...

 I - SPY points: 5

... and some have a combination of the two.

 I - SPY points: 10

Britain's railways have had their own independent police force since the very beginning. Originally, railway policemen also acted as signalmen and controlled the movement of trains. Even today, some railway staff refer to the signalman as 'bobby'. *Do you know why policemen are called bobbies?*

 I - SPY points: 10, double with answer

You may see a traveller with a bicycle...

 I - SPY points: 10

...or a floor engraving.

 I - SPY points: 10

...or a statue.

 I - SPY points: 15

This station roof is huge and comes from a great mainline terminus in a city.

 I - SPY points: 10

This is an example of when old meets new. Note the old tiled station sign and the modern version underneath.

 I - SPY points: 15

You can find comfortable seats to sit while you wait for your train...

 I - SPY points: 10

...pick up some local information...

 I - SPY points: 10

...post a letter...

 I - SPY points: **10**

...or get a permit to travel.

 I - SPY points: **10**

Stations always have facilities if you need to use them.

 I - SPY points: **5**

Here's where you can meet your friends at the end of their journey.

 I - SPY points: **10**

A number of main line stations have courtesy buggies like this one to take disabled or unwell travellers and their luggage to or from the train in comfort.

I - SPY points: 20

There are always plenty of self-help luggage trolleys to save carrying heavy suitcases and bags by hand.

I - SPY points: 10

Some suitcases come complete with their own wheels.

I - SPY points: 10

You may need to get from one level to another by...

...an escalator...

 I - SPY points: 10

...or a lift.

 I - SPY points: 10

Some trains have special access for bicycles...

 I - SPY points: 15

...and others have low level entry for wheelchair access.

 I - SPY points: 15

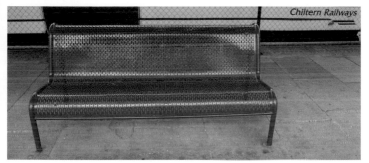

Chiltern Railways

It's always nice to be able to take the weight off your feet and sit down whilst waiting for a train. Modern seats are made from metal and look like this.

 I - SPY points: 5

You can always read a newspaper or magazine whilst you wait...

 I - SPY points: 5

...or make a 'phone call.

 I - SPY points: 5

The guard can punch your ticket.
Why does he do this?

I - SPY points: 5,
double with answer

There is usually a rush to get on
board.

I - SPY points: 5

You may wish to check with the
attendant that this is the right
train...

I - SPY points: 10

You may be leaving someone
special at the station...

I - SPY points: 10

You may be waving goodbye to someone...

 I - SPY points: 10

...before the signal is given, the whistle is blown and the train departs!

 I - SPY points: 20

If you are lucky you may even see the train driver.

 I - SPY points: 10

Many intercity trains carry a restaurant car where travellers can enjoy a full meal, with wine, while on the move.

 I - SPY points: **10**

A fully trained chef will prepare your meal for you...

 I - SPY points: **10**

...and will even serve it to your table.

 I - SPY points: **10**

Or you may just fancy tea and coffee.

 I - SPY points: **10**

Hot snacks and a wide variety of light refreshments are available from the buffet car.

 I - SPY points: 5

Some services offer newspapers.

 I - SPY points: 10

A trolley service brings a selection of drinks and snacks to you at your seat.

 I - SPY points: 10

Communications

It's easy to stay in touch on a train journey. Many stations now offer WiFi facilities...

...for telephones...

 I - SPY points: 15

 I - SPY points: 10

....and laptops. Some business men and women can have a meeting while the train is moving.

 I - SPY points: 15

This woman is working on her laptop computer...

 I - SPY points: 15

...and so is this man.

 I - SPY points: 15

It doesn't have to be work. You can play on the train as well!

 I - SPY points: 15

Interior Features

See how many of these seat configurations you can spot.

 I - SPY points: 5, for each

First Class seats usually have head rest covers bearing the name of the train company operating the service.

 I - SPY points: 10

If you feel you need a rest, you can draw the curtains!

 I - SPY points: 15

It's a good idea to reserve your seat.

 I - SPY points: 15

29

These are all emergency features that you should only use in extreme conditions or under supervision.

In the event of an emergency these posters tell you exactly what to do.

 I - SPY points: 10

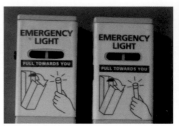

Should the train lose power, you can use the emergency lights provided at the end of the carriage.

 I - SPY points: 10

The alarm handle must only ever be pulled in case of an emergency. It sends a message to the driver to stop the train.

 I - SPY points: 10

Some trains have automatic doors. These open at the push of a button when the train is in a station.

 I - SPY points: 10

Interior Features

Trains are homes on wheels for travellers during their long journeys. Here are just a few things you'll find inside an average railway carriage:

A toilet with washbasin, soap and towels so you can freshen up on a long journey.

 I – SPY points: 5

Luggage racks above the seats and at the end of carriages.

 I – SPY points: 5

Quiet Carriage

Many trains now have a dedicated quiet carriage. This is for people who wish to travel in peace, so no music or telephones in here please!

 I – SPY points: 15

If you want to work (or play) on the train you may need an electricity supply.

 I – SPY points: 10

31

People

All sorts of people need to take train journeys, businessmen and women, students, shoppers, people making a visit and many others. See how many of these you can spot.

 I - SPY points: 5

One of the joys of train travel (especially if you have an I-Spy on a Train Journey to hand) is all the places and things of interest that you can look for through the carriage window as the train rushes through town and country. See how many of these you can Spy and then look out for others of your own.

Poppy fields.

 I - **SPY** points: 5

A gas holder, sometimes called a gasometer.

 I - **SPY** points: 5

A power station, this one has four big cooling towers.

 I - **SPY** points: 5

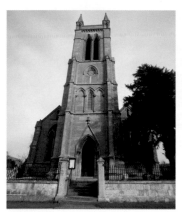

Cathedrals and churches with their high steeples and towers.

 I - SPY points: 5

Trains often pass by rivers when travelling through the countryside.

I - SPY points: 5

Sometimes the train line goes over a motorway or a dual carriageway. like this one.

 I - SPY points: 5

34

A windmill – or a watermill.

 I - **SPY** points: 5

A wind turbine producing electricity.

 I - **SPY** points: 5

Electricity pylons.

 I - **SPY** points: 5

A deer park.

 I - **SPY** points: 5

A castle.

 I - SPY points: 5

A hot air balloon.

 I - SPY points: 5

MICHELIN

*Many railway lines run close to the seashore or near a stretch
of inland water.*

This train is passing a canal.

I - **SPY** points: 15

This train is at a station which
serves a harbour and a large
ferry boat can be seen behind it.

I - **SPY** points: 20

The line may pass a harbour.
*How many boats can
you see?*

I - **SPY** points: 15

Or you may pass along the sea
front and spot a pier.

I - **SPY** points: 15

Bridges and Viaducts

Railway lines are carried across valleys, rivers and roads by a variety or bridges and viaducts.

This graceful viaduct is constructed of stones and has many arches.

 I - SPY points: 10

This National Express train is crossing a wide river.

 I - SPY points: 10

Apart from red signals, there are other occasions where the train driver will need to stop.

Where a line ends in a station or at a siding, there will be a buffer stop. These are often painted red and may have one or more red lights.

 I - SPY points: 5

Sometimes lines may be blocked for engineering work and a temporary stop board will be placed on the line.

 I - SPY points: 10

"Not to be moved" boards are used when the train is being cleaned or if an engineer is working on the train.

 I - SPY points: 15

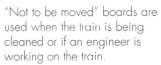

There are two main types of signals used on the UK railway network, colour light signals and mechanical signals (often called semaphores).

These have an arm mounted on a post that can be moved up and down to indicate stop (horizontal) or proceed (raised or lowered). The arms can be red or yellow depending on the function of the signal and there may be more than one arm if there is a junction ahead.

 I - SPY points: 5

This is a distant signal and is showing caution meaning that the driver will have to stop at the next signal.

 I - SPY points: 15

This is a shunting signal. This one shows stop. The disc turns 45 degrees to show proceed. Signals like this are used for trains to move into sidings or to cross from one track to another.

 I - SPY points: 15

This train is passing a two-aspect signal displaying caution (yellow). The next signal will be red and the train will have to stop.

 I - SPY points: 10

At junctions and points where trains need to change tracks, signals are fitted with five white lights (called feathers) to tell the driver which route the train will take. This train is about to cross onto a line to the left of the mainline.

 I - SPY points: 20

This is a modern shunting signal. Two reds means stop. Two white lights at 45 degrees means proceed.

 I - SPY points: 15

You will find this sign at locations near railway lines such as level crossings.

I - SPY points: 10

This sign is found near electrified lines. The cables carry 25,000 volts therefore staff and passengers must keep well away from them.

I - SPY points: 10

Maintenance crews may have to work on the line while trains are running. When a train approaches, they have to get to a "position of safety". In some areas, such as on bridges and in cuttings, there is not much room by the side of the track. This is where you will find a "Limited clearance" sign.

I - SPY points: 25

Like roads, railway lines have varying speed limits. Trains may have to slow down at different locations such as junctions, crossovers, and sharp bends.

This is a triangular advanced warning sign. It tells the driver that the speed indicated applies to the line ahead.

I - SPY points: 10

This circular warning sign indicates the point where the speed limit starts.

I - SPY points: 15

Before the modern circular and triangular warning signs were introduced, metal signs with cut-out numerals were used.

I - SPY points: 20

There are two types of electrified line in the UK. A third rail (750 volts DC) outside the main running rails is used on many lines south of London. The other system uses high voltage overhead power lines (25,000 volts AC) known as catenary.

A pantograph on the roof of a train.

I - SPY points: 20

On single and many double track lines, single masts are usually used to support the overhead wires which zigzag to even out wear on the collector strips on the pantograph.

I - SPY points: 15

Where there are multiple lines, structures such as this one called a headspan are used.

I - SPY points: 15

This commuter train in Kent is using its shoes to pick up power from the third rail which you can see on the outside of the running rails.

 I - **SPY** points: 15

Here you can see the shoe picking up electricity from the third rail.

I **SPY** points: 20

Introduced by British Rail in 1976, the diesel High Speed Train (HST) is still used widely across the country on long distance services. These trains have a top speed of 125mph and have a power car at either end to pull and push the train.

◯ **I - SPY** points: 15

This is a Class 390 Pendolino. These electric trains tilt which means that they can go faster around curves than normal trains and cut journey times. The tilting mechanism makes it more comfortable for passengers. Their maximum speed is currently 125mph although they were designed for 140mph.

◯ **I - SPY** points: 20

This is a class 91 electric locomotive. At the other end of the train is a carriage with a driving cab. The locomotive stays at one end of the train and is controlled from the other end of the train when travelling in the other direction. This is called a push pull train.

 I - SPY points: 20

This is a class 220 Voyager train. These trains and similar class 221 and 222 units were built to replace older trains on routes across the country. The class 221 trains are designed to tilt like the class 390 Pendolino and have a top speed of 125mph.

 I - SPY points: 20

These trains have no separate locomotive but have diesel or electrically powered carriages with a cab at each end. They normally have their number on the front of the cab. The first three digits are the class number.

The Class 185 Desiro has an engine in each carriage, but they do not all need to be used for the whole journey especially if the train is coasting downhill.

 I - SPY points: 15

The Class 170 Turbostar units consist of either two or three carriages. This one is carrying passengers from Stansted Airport to Birmingham.

 I - SPY points: 15

The Class 143 units and the similar class 142 were introduced in the 1980s. They were built as low-cost trains and used many items, such as the seats from buses built by the same companies.

 I - SPY points: 20

The Class 375 Electostar units are used for commuter services in the south of England along with similar units of classes 357, 376 and 377.

 I - SPY points: 15

The Class 395 140mph trains are Britain's fastest domestic trains. The dual voltage units were built in Japan for commuter services from London St Pancras to Kent.

I - SPY points: 15

The modern Class 350 units are part of the Desiro family of trains. They are used on commuter services in London and the southeast and also on the west coast mainline to Birmingham, Crewe and Liverpool. Like the Electrostar, they can be configured to use overhead or third rail power.

 I - SPY points: 15

49

Today, the vast majority of passenger trains are multiple unit trains that do not have a locomotive. However, locomotives are still used on some passenger routes.

I - SPY points: 15

This is a class 08 shunter. These were once the most numerous locomotives on the network as nearly 1,000 of them were built. They have a very low top speed of 15 mph and can easily be identified by their yellow and black "wasp" stripes on the cab and nose end.

I - SPY points: 10

First bought by EWS to replace the life-expired ex-British Rail ones, these diesel locomotives are the most common freight locomotives in use in Britain today.

These 125mph diesel locomotives were built mainly to haul parcels and mail trains around the network. They are currently used to haul sleeper trains.

 I - SPY points: 15

These electric locomotives can be found hauling passenger and freight trains along the electrified network. You may also see them hauling container trains.

I - SPY points: 15

The class 92s are the most modern and sophisticated electric locomotives on the network. They were built to haul international freight and overnight passenger trains from Britain to France.

 I - SPY points: 20

Freight trains carry goods all over the country. They are not as fast as passenger trains so a lot of them run at night.

This train has hopper wagons for carrying coal from collieries and docks to power stations to generate electricity.

 I - SPY points: 15

This train is carrying containers from a port. Huge cranes load the containers from ships onto the wagons.

 I - SPY points: 20

This is a train of tank wagons which are used to carry liquids and powders. These ones are carrying oil from a refinery.

 I - SPY points: 20

Freight trains also carry brand new vehicles from ports and factories.

 I - SPY points: 25

Eurostar™ operates from London's St Pancras International Station and trains transport you to either Paris or Brussels, travelling through the Channel Tunnel at speeds of up to 300km per hour (186mph) on a network of high-speed lines.

The trains that run under the channel are Eurostar's eighteen-carriage Class 373 trains.

I - SPY points: 5, for each

Leaving the Country

To help you get around your destination, modern digital travel guides are available.

 I - SPY points: 15

This is a statue of a famous poet who helped save St Pancras Station from redevelopment in the 1960s.

Do you know his name?

 I - SPY points: 15, double with answer

As well as the Eurostar™, there are other ways to leave the country. There are train services to the major airports. Here are three options.

The Heathrow Express opened in 1998. It provides high speed rail connections from central London's Paddington Station to Heathrow Central (Terminals 1, 2, 3 and 4) and to Heathrow Terminal 5.

 I - SPY points: 15

The Gatwick Express was introduced in 1984. Trains run between London's Victoria Station and Gatwick Airport every 15 minutes. The service takes around 30 minutes.

 I - SPY points: 15

Trains on the Stansted Express also run every 15 minutes but unlike the Gatwick Express, stop at stations between the airport and the final destination, London's Liverpool Street Station.

 I - SPY points: 15

The last steam locomotives to be used for regular services on Britain's railways were withdrawn by British Rail in 1968. Many locomotives were then preserved by groups and individuals. Most of these are based on the preserved lines around the country but a number are permitted to run on the national rail network and can be seen hauling special trains.

Duchess of Sutherland is a preserved ex-LMS steam locomotive. The locomotive is seen here hauling a special from London King's Cross Station to Norwich via Cambridge.

 I - SPY points: 20, for any steam train

The first new steam train to be built in 50 years, the Tornado, took 19 years to complete. Its maiden journey from Darlington to London's King's Cross was in February 2009.

 I - SPY points: 30

The London Underground was the world's first underground railway system. The first section opened in 1863. Several underground train systems in major cities like Paris use Michelin Tyres to run on the rails. This gives a technical advantage as the trains run quieter, can go up steeper inclines and reduce wear on the metal tracks.

This station is above ground level.

 I - SPY points: 5

London Underground has used their famous circular logo for nearly 100 years. Here it is used as a "Way Out" sign.

 I - SPY points: 5

Many of the platforms are deep under London and may require more than one escalator to reach ground level.
Do you know the deepest station on the network?

 I - SPY points: 5, double with answer

Several of the central London platforms are curved. As the train pulls into the station, there are sometimes gaps between the train and the edge of the platform. Be careful!

 I - SPY points: 5

You may need to take the subway to another platform, or to the station exit.

 I - SPY points: 10

Journey's end for some passengers may be a welcome drink at one of the many station inns which have a railway name.

 I - SPY points: 10

You may need to take a taxi to reach your final destination...

 I - SPY points: 5

...or you may need to catch a ferry to reach it!

 I - SPY points: 15

If you are being met at your destination, the arrivals indicator board will tell the person waiting for you when the train is due.

 I - SPY points: 5

The way out of the station is always clearly marked.

 I - SPY points: 5

The tracks into many city centre stations are carried above the streets on low viaducts. The spaces below the arches are often used as workshops and by restaurants.

 I - SPY points: 15

All trains need to be maintained to ensure that they run smoothly and safely. Most of the work is carried out at night so as not to disrupt the system or service.

This train is being checked for general works.

 I - SPY points: 15

Trains, like cars, need to be regularly washed.

 I - SPY points: 15

To avoid any confusion, this train is under clear instruction: "Not to be Moved".

 I - SPY points: 15

60

Apart from the usual passenger and freight trains there are other types of train and rail vehicles which you may see. These special vehicles are often painted yellow.

Breakdown train.
These old passenger carriages have been converted to carry equipment used to re-rail vehicles after a derailment.

 I - SPY points: 20

Water-cannon train.
In the autumn, falling leaves can cause problems on the railway. To prevent this, water-cannon trains travel around the network spraying the track to clean off the leaves.

 I - SPY points: 25

Heavy-duty crane.
Cranes such as this are used for lifting rail vehicles back onto the track.

 I - SPY points: 20

A level crossing is where a road or footpath crosses a railway at the same level. There are over 7,600 of these in the UK. Always take care at level crossings.

Manually controlled gate.
These traditional crossings have gates that are opened and closed by a crossing keeper every time a train passes.

 I - SPY points: 10

Automatic half-barrier.
These crossings have two barriers and therefore do not cover the whole road.

 I - SPY points: 10

Manually controlled barriers.
These crossings have barriers across the whole width of the road.

 I - SPY points: 10

Open crossings.
These crossings have no barriers or gates across the road. They are used where quiet roads meet railway lines with very few trains.

 I - SPY points: 15